A Special Book for You

You're Here for a Reason

Nancy Tillman

FEIWEL AND FRIENDS
NEW YORK

You're here for a reason, you certainly are.
The world would be different without you, by far.

If not for your hands and your eyes and your feet,
the world, like a puzzle, would be incomplete.

STOP

Even the smallest of things that you do
blossom and multiply far beyond you.

A kindness, for instance, may triple for days . . .

or set things in motion in different ways.

It travels much further
than you'll ever know . . .

under the treetops . . .

over the snow . . .

till it's wandered . . .

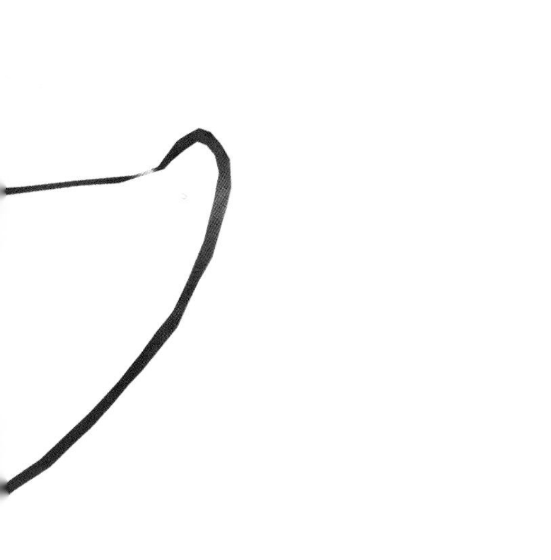

and fluttered . . .

and floated . . .

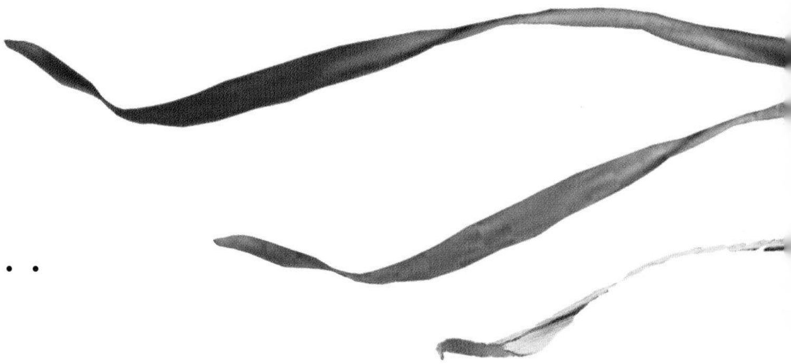

and twirled—

making things happen
all over the world.